C000017638

Animal Antics

Address & Telephone Book

JUDY REINEN

ISBN 1-57977-000-2

Concept and Contents © 1996 Creative Shotz Limited

Animal Antics ™

Published in 1997 by Havoc Publishing Inc.
7868 Silverton Avenue, Suite A
San Diego, California, USA 92126

For further information on other Animal Antics products, please write to us.

Design by Trevor Newman
Printed through Bookbuilders, Hong Kong

Judy Reinen has had a camera in her hands from an early age. Following in her father's footsteps, Judy started Creative Shotz Photography in Auckland, New Zealand, where she has built a reputation for spontaneous wedding and people photography.

Judy loves animals and is passionate about photographing them. She owns a blue point Persian cat called Yabba Dabba Doo, who "purrs so loudly his nickname is Tractor", and a Tibetan terrier named Basil.

"It has been such a pleasure to photograph each dog and cat. I'm constantly being sidetracked - I want to cuddle them all. Each dog and cat has been a star and loved all the fuss. After my Great Dane, Major, passed away, I wished that I had a complete record of his life. I decided to make a series of books so that everyone can have a lifetime of memories of their special friends. Judy has been awarded the prestigious Master of Photography title by the NZ Institute of Professional Photography.

Titles available in the *Animal Antics* series:
Cat Record Book
Dog Record Book
Cat Address & Telephone Book (two formats)
Dog Address & Telephone Book (two formats)

Name:

Address:

Telephone: Fax:

A

Name:

Address:

Telephone/Fax:

Name:

Address:

Telephone/Fax:

Name:

Address:

Telephone/Fax:

Name:

Address:

Telephone   Fax:

Name:

Address:

Telephone: Fax:

Name:

Address:

Telephone: Fax:

A

Name:

Address:

Telephone:/Fax:

Name:

Address:

Telephone:/Fax:

A

Name:
Address:

Telephone: Fax:

Name:
Address:

Telephone: Fax:

Name:
Address:

Telephone: Fax:

Name:
Address:

Telephone: Fax:

Name:
Address:

Telephone: Fax:

B

Name:

Address:

Telephone: Fax:

Name:

Address:

Telephone: Fax:

Name:

Address:

Telephone: Fax:

Name:

Address:

Telephone: Fax:

Name:

Address:

Telephone   Fax:

Name:

Address:

Telephone: Fax:

Name:

Address:

Telephone/Fax:

B

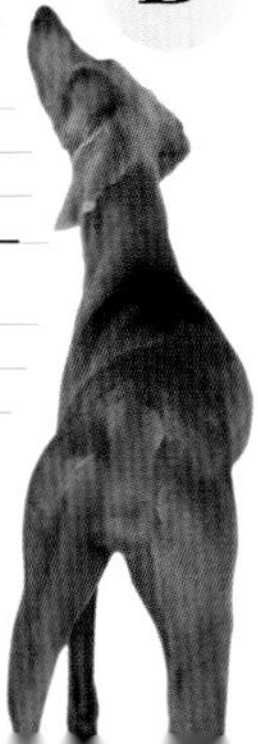

Name:

Address:

Telephone/Fax:

Name:

Address:

Telephone/Fax:

B

Name:

Address:

Telephone: Fax:

Name:

Address:

Telephone: Fax:

Name:

Address:

Telephone: Fax:

Name:

Address:

Telephone: Fax:

Name:

Address:

Telephone: Fax:

Name:

Address:

Telephone: Fax:

Name:

Address:

Telephone: Fax:

Name:

Address:

C

Telephone/Fax:

Name:

Address:

Telephone/Fax:

Name:

Address:

Telephone:/Fax:

Name:

Address:

Telephone: Fax:

Name:

Address:

Telephone: Fax:

Name:

Address:

Telephone: Fax:

C

Name:

Address:

Telephone: Fax:

Name:

Address:

Telephone/Fax:

C

Name:

Address:

Telephone: Fax:

Name:

Address:

Telephone: Fax:

Name:

Address:

Telephone: Fax:

Name:

Address:

Telephone: Fax:

Name:

Address:

Telephone: Fax:

D

Name:

Address:

Telephone: Fax:

Name:

Address:

Telephone: Fax:

D

Name:

Address:

Telephone: Fax:

Name:

Address:

Telephone: Fax:

Name:

Address:

Telephone: Fax:

Name:

Address:

Telephone: Fax:

Name:

Address:

Telephone: Fax:

D

Name:

Address:

Telephone/Fax:

Name:

Address:

Telephone/Fax:

Name:

Address:

Telephone: Fax:

Name:

Address:

Telephone: Fax:

D

Name:

Address:

Telephone: Fax:

Name:

Address:

Telephone: Fax:

Name:

Address:

Telephone: Fax:

E

Name:

Address:

Telephone: Fax:

Name:

Address:

Telephone: Fax:

E

Name:

Address:

Telephone: Fax:

Name:

Address:

Telephone: Fax:

Name:

Address:

Telephone: Fax:

Name:

Address:

Telephone: Fax:

Name:

Address:

Telephone: Fax:

Name:

Address:

Telephone: Fax:

E

Name:

Address:

Telephone: Fax:

Name:

Address:

Telephone: Fax:

Name:

Address:

Telephone: Fax:

E

Name:

Address:

Telephone: Fax:

Name:

Address:

Telephone: Fax:

Name:

Address:

Telephone: Fax:

F

Name: Faulkner
Address: 16 Woods View

Telephone: 754 384   Fax:

Name:
Address:

Telephone: Fax:

Name:
Address:

Telephone: Fax:

Name:
Address:

Telephone: Fax:

Name:
Address:

Telephone: Fax:

Name:

Address:

Telephone: Fax:

Name:

Address:

Telephone: Fax:

F

Name:

Address:

Telephone: Fax:

Name:

Address:

Telephone: Fax:

Name:

Address:

Telephone: Fax:

Name:

Address:

Telephone: Fax:

F

Name:

Address:

Telephone: Fax:

Name:

Address:

Telephone: Fax:

Name:

Address:

Telephone: Fax:

Name:

Address:

Telephone: Fax:

Name:

Address:

Telephone: Fax:

G

Name:

Address:

Telephone: Fax:

Name:

Address:

Telephone: Fax:

Name:

Address:

Telephone: Fax:

Name:

Address:

Telephone: Fax:

Name:

Address:

Telephone: Fax:

Name:

Address:

Telephone: Fax:

G

Name:

Address:

Telephone/Fax:

Name:

Address:

Telephone/Fax:

Name:

Address:

Telephone: Fax:

Name:

Address:

Telephone: Fax:

G

Name:

Address:

Telephone: Fax:

Name:

Address:

Telephone: Fax:

Name:

Address:

Telephone: Fax:

Name: Hardy

Address:

Telephone: 751 393   Fax:

Name:

Address:

Telephone: Fax:

Name:

Address:

H

Telephone: Fax:

Name:

Address:

Telephone/Fax:

Name:

Address:

Telephone/Fax:

Name:

Address:

Telephone: Fax:

Name:

Address:

Telephone: Fax:

Name:

Address:

Telephone: Fax:

H

Name:

Address:

Telephone: Fax:

Name:

Address:

Telephone: Fax:

H

Name:

Address:

Telephone: Fax:

Name:

Address:

Telephone: Fax:

Name:

Address:

Telephone: Fax:

Name:

Address:

Telephone: Fax:

Name:

Address:

Telephone: Fax:

Name:

Address:

Telephone: Fax:

Name:

Address:

Telephone: Fax:

I

Name:

Address:

Telephone: Fax:

Name:

Address:

Telephone: Fax:

Name:

Address:

Telephone: Fax:

Name:

Address:

Telephone: Fax:

Name:

Address:

Telephone: Fax:

J

Name:

Address:

Telephone/Fax:

Name:

Address:

TelephoneFax:

Name:

Address:

Telephone/Fax:

Name:

Address:

Telephone: Fax:

Name:

Address:

Telephone: Fax:

Name:

Address:

Telephone: Fax:

J

Name:

Address:

Telephone: Fax:

Name:

Address:

Telephone: Fax:

Name:

Address:

Telephone: _____ Fax: _____

Name:

Address:

Telephone: _____ Fax: _____

J

Name:

Address:

Telephone: _____ Fax: _____

Name:

Address:

Telephone: _____ Fax: _____

Name:

Address:

Telephone: _____ Fax: _____

Name:

Address:

Telephone: Fax:

Name:

Address:

Telephone: Fax:

K

Name:

Address:

Telephone: Fax:

Name:

Address:

Telephone: Fax:

Name:

Address:

Telephone: Fax:

Name:

Address:

Telephone: Fax:

Name:

Address:

Telephone: Fax:

Name:

Address: **K**

Telephone: Fax:

Name:

Address:

Telephone: Fax:

Name:

Address:

Telephone: Fax:

K

Name:

Address:

Telephone: Fax:

Name:

Address:

Telephone: Fax:

Name:

Address:

Telephone: Fax:

Name:

Address:

Telephon/Fax:

Name:

Address:

Telephone: Fax:

L

Name:

Address:

Telephone: Fax:

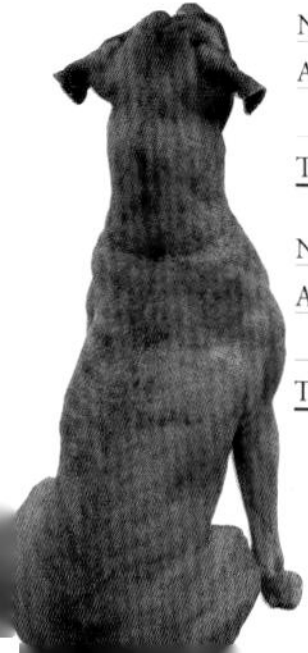

Name:

Address:

Telephone: Fax:

Name:

Address:

Telephone: Fax:

Name:

Address:

Telephone: Fax:

Name:

Address:

Telephone: Fax:

Name:

Address:

L

Telephone: Fax:

Name:

Address:

Telephone/Fax:

Name:

Address:

Telephone/Fax:

L

Name:

Address:

Telephone: Fax:

Name:

Address:

Telephone: Fax:

Name:

Address:

Telephone: Fax:

Name:

Address:

Telephone: Fax:

Name:

Address:

Telephone: Fax:

Name:

Address:

Telephone: Fax:

Name:

Address:

Telephone: Fax:

M

Name:

Address:

Telephone: Fax:

Name:

Address:

Telephone: Fax:

Name:

Address:

Telephone: Fax:

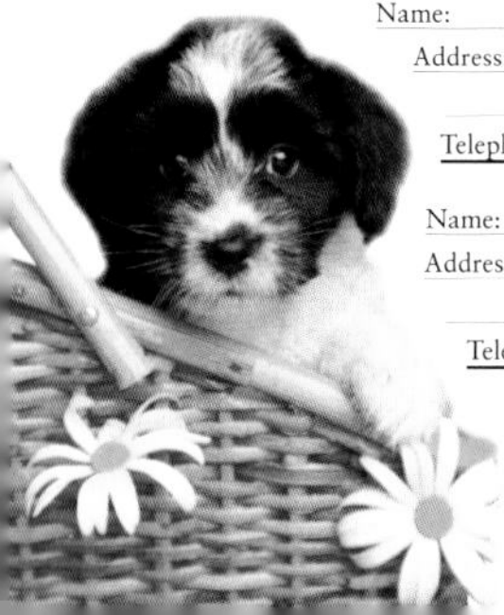

Name:

Address:

Telephone: Fax:

Name:

Address:

Telephone: Fax:

Name:

Address:

Telephone: Fax:

M

Name:

Address:

Telephone: Fax:

Name:

Address:

Telephone/Fax:

M

Name:
Address:

Telephone: Fax:

Name:
Address:

Telephone: Fax:

Name:
Address:

Telephone: Fax:

Name:
Address:

Telephone: Fax:

Name:
Address:

Telephone: Fax:

N

Name:

Address:

Telephone: Fax:

Name:

Address:

Telephone: Fax:

Name:

Address:

Telephone: Fax:

Name:

Address:

Telephone: Fax:

Name:

Address:

Telephone: Fax:

Name:

Address:

Telephone: Fax:

Name:

Address:

Telephone: Fax:

Name:

Address:

Telephone: Fax:

N

Name:

Address:

Telephone: Fax:

Name:

Address:

Telephone: Fax:

N

Name:

Address:

Telephone: Fax:

Name:

Address:

Telephone: Fax:

Name:

Address:

Telephone: Fax:

O

O

Name:

Address:

Telephone: Fax:

Name:

Address:

Telephone: Fax:

Name:

Address:

Telephone: Fax:

Name:

Address:

Telephone: Fax:

Name:

Address:

Telephone: Fax:

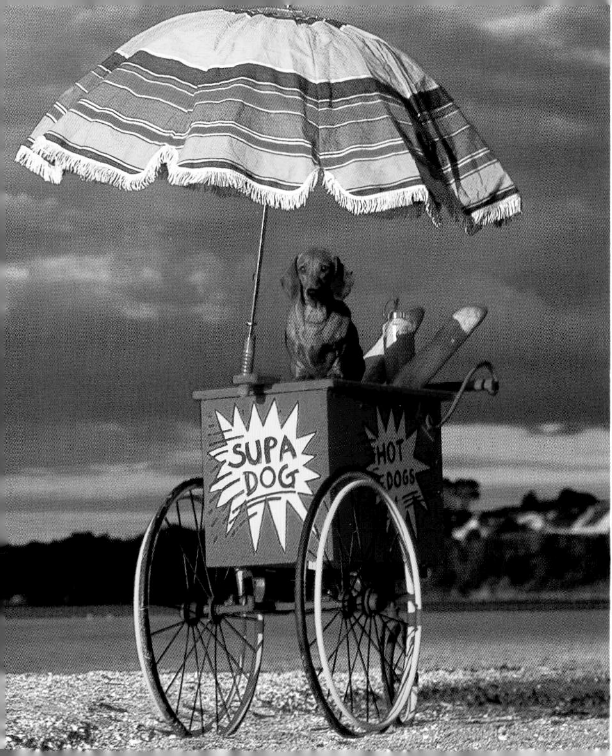

P

Name:

Address:

Telephone: Fax:

Name:

Address:

Telephone: Fax:

P

Name:

Address:

Telephone: Fax:

Name:

Address:

Telephone: Fax:

Name:

Address:

Telephone: Fax:

Name:

Address:

Telephone: Fax:

Name:

Address:

Telephone: Fax:

Name:

Address:

Telephone: Fax:

P

P

Name:

Address:

Telephone: Fax:

Name:

Address:

Telephone: Fax:

Name:

Address:

Telephone: Fax:

Name:

Address:

Telephone: Fax:

Name:

Address:

Telephone: Fax:

Name:

Address:

Telephone: Fax:

Name:

Address:

Telephone: Fax:

Q

Name:

Address:

Telephone: Fax:

Name:

Address:

Telephone: Fax:

Name:

Address:

Telephone: Fax:

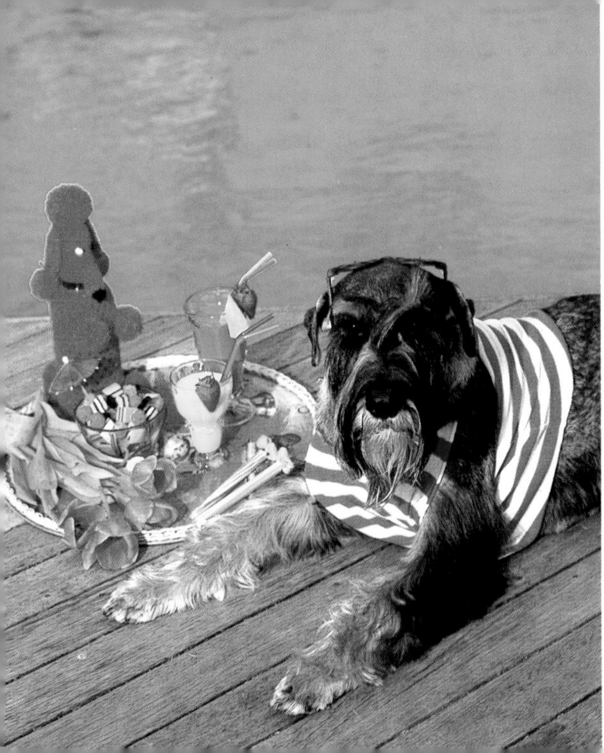

(R)

Name:

Address:

Telephone: Fax:

Name:

Address:

Telephone: Fax:

R

Name:

Address:

Telephone: Fax:

Name:

Address:

Telephone: Fax:

Name: _____

Address: _____

Telephone: _____ Fax: _____

Name: _____

Address: _____

Telephone: _____ Fax: _____

Name: _____

Address: _____

R

Telephone: _____ Fax: _____

Name: _____

Address: _____

Telephone: _____ Fax: _____

Name: _____

Address: _____

Telephone: _____ Fax: _____

R

Name:

Address:

Telephone: Fax:

Name:

Address:

Telephone: Fax:

Name:

Address:

Telephone: Fax:

Name:

Address:

Telephone: Fax:

Name:

Address:

Telephone: Fax:

Name: Sam
Address: 10 Telford Ct
Streatham Hill SW2 4
Telephone: Fax:

Name:
Address:

Telephone: Fax:

Name:
Address:

S

Telephone: Fax:

Name:
Address:

Telephone: Fax:

Name:

Address:

Telephone: Fax:

Name:

Address:

Telephone: Fax:

Name:

Address:

S

Telephone: Fax:

Name:

Address:

Telephone: Fax:

S

Name:

Address:

Telephone: Fax:

Name:

Address:

Telephone: Fax:

Name:

Address:

Telephone: Fax:

Name:

Address:

Telephone: Fax:

Name:

Address:

Telephone: Fax:

T

T

Name:

Address:

Telephone: Fax:

Name:

Address:

Telephone: Fax:

Name:

Address:

Telephone: Fax:

Name:

Address:

Telephone: Fax:

Name:

Address:

Telephone: Fax:

Name:

Address:

Telephone: Fax:

Name:

Address:

Telephone: Fax:

T

Name:

Address:

Telephone: Fax:

Name:

Address:

Telephone: Fax:

T

Name:

Address:

Telephone: Fax:

Name:

Address:

Telephone: Fax:

Name:

Address:

Telephone: Fax:

Name:

Address:

Telephone: Fax:

Name:

Address:

Telephone: Fax:

U

Name:

Address:

Telephone: Fax:

Name:

Address:

Telephone: Fax:

Name:

Address:

Telephone: Fax:

Name:

Address:

Telephone: Fax:

Name:

Address:

Telephone: Fax:

V

Name:

Address:

Telephone: Fax:

Name:

Address:

Telephone: Fax:

Name:

Address:

Telephone: Fax:

Name:

Address:

Telephone: Fax:

Name:

Address:

Telephone: Fax:

Name:

Address:

Telephone: Fax:

Name:

Address:

Telephone: Fax:

W

Name:

Address:

Telephone: Fax:

Name:

Address:

Telephone/Fax:

Name:

Address:

Telephone/Fax:

Name:

Address:

Telephone: Fax:

Name:

Address:

Telephone: Fax:

Name:

Address:

Telephone: Fax:

Name:

Address:

Telephone/Fax:

Name:

Address:

Telephone/Fax:

Name:

Address:

Telephone: Fax:

Name:

Address:

Telephone: Fax:

Name:

Address:

Telephone: Fax:

Name:

Address:

Telephone: Fax:

Name:

Address:

Telephone: Fax: